THE ULTIMATE
EVERTON FC
TRIVIA BOOK

A Collection of Amazing Trivia Quizzes
and Fun Facts for Die-Hard Toffees Fans!

Ray Walker

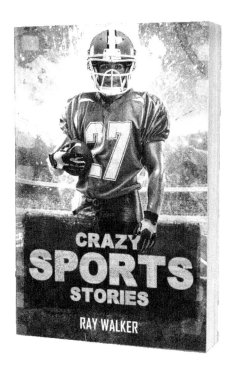

CONTENTS

INTRODUCTION

While Everton FC may not have achieved as much on-pitch success as their neighbors Liverpool FC over the years, the Merseyside club still boasts a very proud and intriguing history.

The roots of this famous team stretch back to 1878, when the St. Domingo FC church team was formed. After proving to be so popular with Liverpudlians, the name was changed a year later to Everton FC to enable more city residents to enjoy the club.

Known as "The Toffees" and "The Blues" by many fans, the club was a founding member of the English Football League in 1888-89 and has been relegated just twice since the league's inaugural campaign.

The Toffees didn't take long to leave a wonderful taste in their supporters' mouths as they captured the First Division title in just the third year of the league. The squad's first FA Cup triumph was then celebrated just over a decade later.

Everton also achieved success on the continent when hoisting the European Cup Winners' Cup in 1984-85 after a brilliant display against Rapid Vienna in Rotterdam.

The team's loyal fans have stuck with the team through thick and thin and are still waiting for the day the entertaining club can capture the League Cup and a Premier League crown.

Everton fans have had the pleasure of witnessing some of the world's top players and youngsters suit up for the squad over the years, with stars such as: Howard Kendall, Duncan Ferguson, Neville Southall, Ted Sagar, Graeme Sharp, Alan Ball, Dixie Dean, Bob Latchford, Thomas Lawton, Wayne Rooney, Joe Royle, Romelu Lukaku, Tim Cahill, Edgar Chadwick, Steven Pienaar, Tony Cottee, and Jose Baxter.

This trivia book has been written to celebrate Everton's colorful history by re-living the club's trials and tribulations from day one to March 2021.

You'll also be able to meet the team's most beloved players and managers and how they have each left their individual mark on the club.

The Toffees' story is told here in a tantalizing quiz form with 12 different quiz chapters each representing a different topic. All sections feature 20 provocative quiz questions along with 10 educational "Did you Know?" facts. The questions are presented in multiple-choice and true-false formats, and the answers are available on a separate page.

We feel this is the ideal way to challenge yourself on the amazing history of Everton FC and to refresh your memory regarding the most famous players and events. The book will hopefully be the perfect training tool for each of your upcoming Everton trivia challenges.

CHAPTER 1:

ORIGINS & HISTORY

QUIZ TIME!

1. What year was the club founded?

    a. 1885
    b. 1883
    c. 1878
    d. 1768

2. Everton was originally founded as St. Domingo FC.

    a. True
    b. False

3. The side's first recorded match was against which team?

    a. St. George's Chapel Football Club
    b. Liverpool Athletics
    c. Millwall FC
    d. Everton Church Club

4. What was the outcome of the team's first recorded game?

    a. draw
    b. 3-3 draw

   c. win

   d. loss

5. Which league did the club first play in?

   a. The Combination

   b. The Football League

   c. The Southern League

   d. The Football Alliance

6. Who did Everton play in their first-ever Football League game?

   a. Blackburn Rovers

   b. Notts County FC

   c. Aston Villa

   d. Accrington FC

7. Everton once played their home games at Anfield, the current home of Liverpool FC.

   a. True

   b. False

8. What was the club's original kit color?

   a. White and blue stripes

   b. Green

   c. Red

   d. Black and scarlet

9. What was the outcome of Everton's first Football League game?

   a. win

   b. 2-2 draw

c. 2-1 win

d. loss

10. Which is one of the club's nicknames?

    a. The Watchmen

    b. The Toffees

    c. The Boys in Blue

    d. The Mints

11. What is the centerpiece of Everton's crest?

    a. Everton townhall building

    b. A lighthouse

    c. A castle watchtower

    d. The Everton lock-up

12. Everton was a founding member of the Premier League.

    a. True

    b. False

13. Everton played their first-ever Premier League game against which club?

    a. Sheffield Wednesday

    b. Norwich City FC

    c. Tottenham Hotspur

    d. Nottingham Forest FC

14. How many games did Everton win in their first Football League season?

    a. 17

    b. 12

c. 9

d. 7

15. Which club did Everton win their first Premier League game against?

a. Chelsea FC

b. Coventry City FC

c. Ipswich Town

d. Manchester United

16. Everton was a founding member of the English Football League in 1888-89.

a. True

b. False

17. Which player scored the first goal in the Football League for Everton?

a. Edgar Chadwick

b. George Fleming

c. Nick Ross

d. Robert Watson

18. How many times has Everton been relegated as of 2020?

a. 1

b. 2

c. 5

d. 6

19. Who scored Everton's first goal in the Premier League?

a. Paul Rideout

b. Anthony Cottee

c. Peter Beardsley

d. Barry Horne

20. Everton was first relegated in 1898-99.

a. True

b. False

QUIZ ANSWERS

1. C – 1878

2. A – True

3. D – Everton Church Club

4. C – 1-0 win

5. B – The Football League

6. D – Accrington FC

7. A – True

8. A – White and blue stripes

9. C – 2-1 win

10. B – The Toffees

11. D – The Everton lock-up

12. A – True

13. A – Sheffield Wednesday

14. C – 9

15. D – Manchester United

16. A – True

17. B – George Fleming

18. B – 2

19. D – Barry Horne

20. B – False

DID YOU KNOW?

1. The Everton Football Club is located in Liverpool, England, and currently plays in the country's top-tier Premier League. The club was originally founded in 1878 with its nicknames being "The Toffees" and "The Blues." The current home ground of Everton FC is Goodison Park with a capacity of 39,572, and the club is owned by Farhad Moshiri.

2. The club's original name in 1878 was St. Domingo FC. It was formed to give members of the congregation of St. Domingo Methodist New Connexion Chapel a sport to play during the winters as they played cricket in the summers. The side's first recorded match was a 1-0 win against Everton Church Club.

3. St. Domingo FC changed its name to Everton FC in November 1879. The club was named after a local area of Liverpool, and the name change was due to the fact that people outside of St. Domingo Church wanted to participate. The club motto is "Nil Satis, Nisi Optimum," which translates in English to "Nothing but the best is good enough."

4. Everton was one of the founding members of the English Football League in 1888-89 and has competed in the top-tier of the league since last being relegated and playing in the second-tier in 1953-54. In total, the club has played

every season but four in the top-tier. These were the 1930-31, 1951-52, 1952-53, and 1953-54 campaigns.

5. The squad won its first top-tier League Championship in 1890-91 season and its first FA Cup in 1905-06. The team's supporters are known as "Blues" or "Evertonians." The team's current home colors are royal blue shirts with white shorts and socks.

6. The outbreak of World War I in 1914 interrupted the football league and would do so again when World War II broke out in 1939. Everton was relegated after the 1929-30 season but quickly rebounded and was promoted back to the top-flight a year later, after winning the Second Division.

7. The side was relegated for the second time after the 1950-51 season and played three consecutive seasons in the Second Division. The club was then promoted following the 1953-54 campaign, after finishing as Second Division runner-up. Since then, Everton has played exclusively in the top-flight.

8. The club's first success in Europe came in the 1984-85 season when it hoisted the European Cup Winners' Cup. Everton then became one of the original founding members of the English Premier League in its inaugural 1992-93 campaign.

9. Everton's main rivalry is with Liverpool FC, whose home stadium at Anfield is located just under a mile away from Everton's Goodison Park venue. Meetings between the

two sides are known as The Merseyside Derby. Everton also used to play at Anfield until 1892 but moved to Goodison Park following a disagreement over the rent at Anfield.

10. The Everton FC women's club currently competes in the FA Women's Super League, which is the top division of English women's football. The club was originally formed in 1983 as Hoylake W.F.C. and became Everton Ladies in 1995. It plays its home games at Walton Hall Park. As of March 2021, the side had won the Premier League National Division once, the Premier League Cup once, and the Women's FA Cup twice.

CHAPTER 2:

THE CAPTAIN CLASS

QUIZ TIME!

1. Who was the first official full-time captain of the club?

    a. John Holt
    b. Bob Howarth
    c. Andrew Hannah
    d. Nick Ross

2. Séamus Coleman has captained the Irish men's national team since 2012.

    a. True
    b. False

3. Billy Wright captained which club after leaving Everton?

    a. Blackburn Rovers
    b. Preston North End
    c. Watford FC
    d. Birmingham City FC

4. Who has been the Toffees' longest-serving skipper as of 2020?

   a. Hunter Hart

   b. Mick Lyons

   c. Peter Farrell

   d. Kevin Ratcliffe

5. Who did Phil Neville replace as captain?

   a. Jimmy Settle

   b. Duncan Ferguson

   c. Alan Stubbs

   d. David Weir

6. Who was Everton's first skipper in the Premier League?

   a. Dave Watson

   b. Kevin Ratcliffe

   c. Gary Speed

   d. Peter Beardsley

7. Everton has had 40 full-time captains as of 2020.

   a. True

   b. False

8. Which club did David Weir captain after leaving Everton?

   a. Brighton Hove & Albion FC

   b. Glasgow Rangers FC

   c. Arsenal FC

   d. Aberdeen FC

9. Which year did Mick Lyons become club skipper?

a. 1974

b. 1976

c. 1978

d. 1980

10. Who did Duncan Ferguson replace as captain?

    a. Dave Watson

    b. Gary Speed

    c. Kevin Campbell

    d. Mark Higgins

11. Which player captained Everton to their first league championship?

    a. Jimmy Galt

    b. Richard Boyle

    c. Andrew Hannah

    d. Warney Cresswell

12. Dave Watson had two spells as club captain.

    a. True

    b. False

13. Who was club captain in 1953-54 when the team earned promotion back to the First Division?

    a. Roy Vernon

    b. Peter Farrell

    c. Norman Greenhalgh

    d. TE Jones

14. Who captained Everton to their first FA Cup trophy?

a. Billy Cook

b. Dixie Dean

c. Tom Booth

d. Jack Taylor

15. How many matches did Gary Speed captain the Welsh men's national team?

a. 30

b. 37

c. 44

d. 50

16. Alan Ball captained the club in its first UEFA competition.

a. True

b. False

17. Who did Séamus Coleman replace as captain?

a. Phil Neville

b. Alan Stubbs

c. Phil Jagielka

d. David Weir

18. What year was Kevin Ratcliffe given the Toffees' armband?

a. 1982

b. 1984

c. 1986

d. 1988

19. Alan Ball joined which club from Everton and was named club captain?

a. Sunderland AFC

b. Southampton FC

c. Blackpool FC

d. Arsenal FC

20. Phil Jagielka was the first Everton player to captain the English men's national team.

   a. True

   b. False

QUIZ ANSWERS

1. D – Nick Ross

2. B – False

3. D – Birmingham City FC

4. C – Peter Farrell

5. D – David Weir

6. A – Dave Watson

7. B – False

8. B – Glasgow Rangers FC

9. B – 1976

10. C – Kevin Campbell

11. C – Andrew Hannah

12. A – True

13. B – Peter Farrell

14. D – Jack Taylor

15. C – 44

16. B – False

17. C – Phil Jagielka

18. B – 1984

19. D – Arsenal FC

20. A – True

DID YOU KNOW?

1. As of March 2021, Everton has had 45 different full-time appointed club captains throughout its history, with Nick Ross being the first and Séamus Coleman being the most recent. The following players wore the armband between 1888 and World War I: Nick Ross 1888-89; Andrew Hannah 1889-91; John Holt 1891-93; Bob Howarth 1893-94; Richard Boyle 1894-96; Billy Stewart 1896-97; Richard Boyle 1897-98; Jack Taylor 1898-1900; Jimmy Settle 1900-01; Tom Booth 1901-04; William Balmer 1904-05; Jack Taylor 1905-08; Jack Sharp 1908-10; Harry Makepeace 1910-11; John Maconnachie 1911-14; Jimmy Galt 1914-15.

2. Those who skippered the side between 1919 and the beginning of the Premier League era were: Tom Fleetwood 1919-20; Dickie Downs 1920-21; John McDonald 1921-22; Hunter Hart 1922-27; Warney Cresswell 1927-29; Hunter Hart 1929-30; Ben Williams 1930-31; Dixie Dean 1931-37; Billy Cook 1937-38; Jock Thomson 1938-39; Norman Greenhalgh 1946-48; Peter Farrell 1948-57; TE Jones 1957-61; Roy Vernon 1961-65; Brian Labone 1965-70; Alan Ball 1970-71; Howard Kendall 1972-74; Roger Kenyon 1974-76; Mick Lyons 1976-82; Billy Wright 1982; Mark Higgins 1983-84; Kevin Ratcliffe 1984-92.

3. Everton players who wore the armband from the beginning of the Premier League era in 1992-93 to March

2021 have been: Dave Watson 1992-97; Gary Speed 1997-98; Dave Watson 1998-2001; Kevin Campbell 2001-02; Duncan Ferguson 2002-04; Alan Stubbs 2004-05; David Weir 2005-06; Phil Neville 2007-13; Phil Jagielka 2013-19; Séamus Coleman 2019-present.

4. Nick Ross of Scotland was the captain during the inaugural Football League season in 1888-89. He previously skippered Heart of Midlothian before joining Preston North End where he was converted from center-forward to left-back and was also captain. He joined Everton in July 1888 and was one of the best-paid players at a reported £10 a month. Ross became the first full-back to score a league goal but played just one season with the Toffees before returning to Preston. He retired in 1893 and passed away the following year from tuberculosis at the age of 31. Ross's brother Jimmy also played with Preston and topped the First Division in scoring in 1890-91.

5. When Everton won the First Division title for the first time in 1890-91, Andrew Hannah of Scotland was the club skipper. The right-back played with the team from 1889 to 1891 and missed just two games in the side's title-winning campaign after finishing as runner-up the previous season. He joined from Renton and returned there after leaving the Toffees, and in 1892, Hannah became the first recognized captain of Liverpool.

6. Jack Taylor was the first Everton captain to hoist the FA Cup after the side beat Newcastle United in the 1905-06

final. The Scottish international midfielder played with the club from 1896 to 1910 after arriving from St. Mirren. He played over 450 times for the side and wore the armband between 1898 and 1900 and again from 1905 to 1908.

7. With 494 Everton appearances under his belt between 1980 and 1992, Welsh international defender Kevin Ratcliffe currently ranks fifth on the club's all-time appearance list. He joined as an apprentice in 1977 and made his debut in 1980. Ratcliffe was captain between 1984 and 1992 and led the side to the 1983-84 FA Cup, the First Division title in 1984-85 and 1986-87, and the European Cup Winners' Cup in 1984-85. His sides also earned runner-up medals in three other FA Cup finals and a League Cup final and won three FA Charity Shields and shared another. Ratcliffe joined Dundee United in 1991 and later became a football manager.

8. The last Everton skipper to hoist any major silverware was Dave Watson when the side won the 1994-95 FA Cup and the 1995 FA Charity Shield. The English international joined from Norwich City in 1986 and is currently third on the team's all-time appearance list, with 528 games. He wore the armband between 1992 and 1997 and remained with the club until hanging up his boots in 2001. Watson also helped the side win the First Division in 1986-87 and the 1987 Charity Shield. He also managed the club briefly in March 1997 when Joe Royle resigned and would later manage Tranmere Rovers.

9. Hometown defender Mick Lyons played with the Toffees from 1971 to 1982 to kick off his pro career and appeared in 472 games while chipping in with 59 goals. He was the club's captain from 1976 to 1982 before moving to Sheffield Wednesday. Lyons didn't manage to win any trophies with the side but took home a 1976-77 League Cup runner-up medal. He also led the team in scoring in 1973-74 with nine goals. After hanging up his boots, Lyons managed the Brunei men's national team as well as club sides in Canada and Australia.

10. Welsh international midfielder and skipper Gary Speed joined Everton from Leeds United in 1996 for a reported £3.5 million. He scored on his debut and finished the campaign with 11 goals to share the team lead with Duncan Ferguson. He took over the captain's armband in 1997-98, but his relationship with manager Howard Kendall worsened, and he was sold to Newcastle United for a reported £5.5 million in January 1998. Speed played 85 times for Wales and made 840 domestic league appearances in his career. He later managed Sheffield United and Wales and sadly took his own life in November 2011, at the age of 42.

CHAPTER 3:

AMAZING MANAGERS

QUIZ TIME!

1. Approximately how many full-time and caretaker managers has Everton had as of 2020?

    a. 15
    b. 18
    c. 21
    d. 30

2. Howard Kendall was the first Everton manager to win the Premier League Manager of the Month award.

    a. True
    b. False

3. Who was regarded as the club's first full-time secretary-manager?

    a. Dick Molyneux
    b. William Edward Barclay
    c. W.J. Sawyer
    d. Theo Kelly

4. Harry Catterick left Everton to manage which club?

    a. Leeds United
    b. Crystal Palace FC
    c. Bristol Rovers FC
    d. Preston North End

5. Who was the first Everton manager to win the LMA Manager of the Year award?

    a. Joe Royle
    b. David Moyes
    c. Howard Kendall
    d. Roberto Martínez

6. Which was the first club David Moyes managed after leaving Everton?

    a. FC Porto
    b. Manchester United
    c. FC Shalke 04
    d. FC Bologna

7. Former Everton secretary-manager William Edward Barclay became the first manager of Liverpool FC.

    a. True
    b. False

8. In terms of silverware won, who is the Toffees' most successful manager as of 2020?

    a. Harry Catterick
    b. Howard Kendall

c. Thomas H. McIntosh

d. David Moyes

9. Marco Silva left which club to manage Everton?

a. Sunderland AFC

b. Watford FC

c. CF Valencia

d. S.C. Salgueiros

10. Who was the club's first manager born outside of the British Isles?

a. Ronald Koeman

b. Marco Silva

c. Roberto Martínez

d. Carlo Ancelotti

11. How many pieces of Football League silverware did Harry Catterick win with Everton?

a. 4

b. 7

c. 5

d. 3

12. W.J. Sawyer never managed Everton in any competitive matches due to the outbreak of the First World War.

a. True

b. False

13. How many times did David Moyes win the LMA Manager of the Year award?

a. 1

b. 3

c. 5

d. 6

14. Which manager led Everton to their first FA Cup trophy?

    a. W.J. Sawyer

    b. Theo Kelly

    c. Dick Molyneux

    d. Will Cuff

15. How many trophies did Howard Kendall win with Everton?

    a. 3

    b. 5

    c. 7

    d. 10

16. Everton was managed by committees between 1935 and 1939.

    a. True

    b. False

17. Carlo Ancelotti left which side to manage Everton?

    a. Chelsea FC

    b. FC Barcelona

    c. S.S.C. Napoli

    d. Borussia Mönchengladbach

18. Who was the first manager to win a trophy with the Toffees in the Premier League era?

    a. Mike Walker
    b. Joe Royle
    c. Walter Smith
    d. Ronald Koeman

19. How many divisional championships did Thomas H. McIntosh win with Everton?

    a. 6
    b. 3
    c. 7
    d. 2

20. Thomas H. McIntosh managed Everton for eight years.

    a. True
    b. False

QUIZ ANSWERS

1. D – 30

2. A – True

3. B – William Edward Barclay

4. D – Preston North End

5. B – David Moyes

6. B – Manchester United

7. A – True

8. B – Howard Kendall

9. B – Watford FC

10. C – Roberto Martínez

11. C – 5

12. A – True

13. B – 3

14. D – Will Cuff

15. C – 7

16. A – True

17. C – S.S.C. Napoli

18. B – Joe Royle

19. B – 3

20. B – False

DID YOU KNOW?

1. The club has had approximately 30 different full-time and caretaker managers/secretaries since being formed, with William Edward Barclay being the first in 1888. The club's current manager, as of March 2021, is Carlo Ancelotti, who was appointed on December 21, 2019. Ancelotti took over from caretaker boss Duncan Ferguson who ran the club after Marco Silva was released on December 5.

2. William Edward Barclay was listed as the club's secretary during its first first season in the newly formed English Football League. Barclay of Dublin, Ireland, was in charge for 22 official matches and then replaced by Dick Molyneux for the 1889-90 campaign. Barclay then went on to become the first manager of Liverpool FC in 1892.

3. Dick Molyneux of England won the first title with the club as he guided it to the First Division championship in the 1890-91 season after finishing as runner-up the year before. He joined Everton in 1878 when the club was still St. Domingo FC and became secretary-manager in August 1889. Molyneaux's side was also runner-up in the league in 1894-95 and reached the FA Cup final in 1892-93 and 1896-97. His stint came to an end in September 1901, after being suspended by the board of directors for suspected drunkenness. He also won nine Liverpool Senior Cups and two Lancashire Senior Cups.

4. When Dick Molyneaux was released in 1901, William C. Cuff of England took over and won the club's first FA Cup in 1905-06 with a 1-0 victory over Newcastle United. He reached the FA Cup final again the next season, then led the side to the First Division crown in 1914-15. Cuff remained on the job for close to 500 games and eventually stepped down in 1918. He then served as chairman of Everton from 1921 to 1938.

5. The club was run by Thomas McIntosh of England between 1919 and 1935 as its secretary, and he was in charge for over 700 games. The team topped the First Division in 1927-28 but was relegated to the Second Division after the 1929-30 campaign. They won the division in 1930-31 to move back to the top-flight. The team then won the First Division the very next season and captured the FA Cup in 1932-33. McIntosh also won the FA Charity Shield in 1928 and 1932 and was runner-up in 1933. He passed away in October 1935, at the age of 56.

6. Everton was run by committee between May 1935 and June 1939, with the team capturing the First Division in 1938-39. The league was put on hold until 1946 because of World War II, and when it resumed, Theo Kelly was still in charge after being appointed in 1939. Some historians view Kelly as the club's first official manager, and he was in charge for 100 games with a record of 38 wins, 19 draws, and 43 losses for a 38.0 winning percentage. He stepped down in 1946 and returned to his post as club secretary.

7. In 1961, Harry Catterick was appointed manager, and he led the club to the First Division title in 1962-63 and 1969-70. He also guided the players to an FA Cup triumph in 1965-66, with a a 3-2 victory over Sheffield Wednesday at Wembley, and won the FA Charity Shield in 1963 and 1970. Catterick managed 594 games with a mark of 276 wins, 157 draws, and 161 losses for a 46.46 winning percentage. He then accepted another job with the club in April 1973.

8. Former Everton player Howard Kendall took over in May 1981 as player-manager for his first of three stints as club boss. He hung up his boots after just four games and then guided the side to the European Cup Winners' Cup and the First Division title in 1984-85. The team won the First Division again in 1986-87, and Kendall won the 1984 and 1985 FA Charity Shield and shared it in 1986 while being named the English Manager of the Year for 1984-85 and 1986-87. He left in the summer of 1987 but returned from November 1990 to December 1993. Kendall then returned to Everton for the third time as manager in August 1997 but left by mutual consent at the end of the season. He managed 542 games in total, with 257 wins, 131 draws, and 154 defeats for a 47.41 winning percentage.

9. The first manager to hail from outside the British Isles was Roberto Martínez of Spain. The former boss of Swansea City and Wigan Athletic took over in May 2013. He was in charge for three seasons, with his final campaign in 2015-16, resulting in Everton posting their worst-ever home

record in history. However, the team reached the semifinals of both the FA Cup and League Cup. Still, Martínez was sacked on the final day of the season and was replaced by Ronald Koeman of Holland. Martínez managed 143 games, with a record of 61 victories, 39 draws, and 43 defeats for a 42.86 winning percentage. He then became manager of Belgium after leaving Goodison Park.

10. The last manager to win silverware with Everton was Joe Royle. The former Everton and England striker, who won the First Division title with the team as a player, took over in November 1994 from Mike Walker after spending 12 years as boss of Oldham Athletic. His side beat Manchester United 1-0 in the 1994-95 FA Cup final and then captured the 1995 FA Charity Shield by edging Blackburn Rovers 1-0. Royle resigned in March 1997, after a disagreement with chairman Peter Johnson over transfers. He went on to manage Manchester City and Ipswich Town before returning to Oldham.

CHAPTER 4:

GOALTENDING GREATS

QUIZ TIME!

1. Which keeper made the most appearances in all competitions for Everton?

   a. Ted Sagar
   b. Neville Southall
   c. Tim Howard
   d. Gordon West

2. Tim Howard made 121 appearances for the American men's national team.

   a. True
   b. False

3. Which player made 34 appearances in the 1999-2000 Premier League?

   a. Richard Wright
   b. Steve Simonsen
   c. Thomas Myhre
   d. Paul Gerrard

4. How many clean sheets did Jordan Pickford keep in the 2018-19 Premier League?

   a. 9

   b. 14

   c. 6

   d. 11

5. Which club did Neville Southall leave to join Everton?

   a. Shrewsbury Town FC

   b. Dover Athletic

   c. Bury FC

   d. Stoke City

6. Which player made 19 appearances behind Joel Robles in the 2016-17 domestic league?

   a. Maarten Stekelenburg

   b. Tim Howard

   c. Jordan Pickford

   d. Iain Turner

7. Tim Howard became the fourth keeper in Premier League history to score a goal.

   a. True

   b. False

8. How many clean sheets did Paul Gerrard record in the 2000-01 domestic league?

   a. 12

   b. 5

c. 10

d. 8

9. Nigel Martyn joined the Toffees from which club?

    a. Queens Park Rangers

    b. Nottingham Forest

    c. Wycombe Wanderers

    d. Leeds United

10. How many appearances did Ted Sagar make for Everton in all competitions?

    a. 522

    b. 500

    c. 462

    d. 336

11. Which club did Gordon West leave Everton for?

    a. Bolton Wanderers

    b. Colchester United

    c. Newport County AFC

    d. Tranmere Rovers

12. Jason Kearton played in Everton's first Premier League match.

    a. True

    b. False

13. Which club did Jordan Pickford leave to join Everton?

    a. Portsmouth FC

    b. Watford FC

c. Sunderland AFC

d. Bristol Rovers FC

14. How many appearances did Neville Southall make in all competitions?

    a. 529

    b. 683

    c. 750

    d. 776

15. Which player made 33 appearances in the 2002-03 domestic league?

    a. Steve Simonsen

    b. Espen Baardsen

    c. Migel Martyn

    d. Richard Wright

16. Tim Howard appeared in every Premier League match for Everton between 2007-08 and 2013-14.

    a. True

    b. False

17. How many clean sheets did Tim Howard keep with Everton in all competitions?

    a. 97

    b. 114

    c. 133

    d. 142

18. How many clean sheets did Neville Southall keep in all competitions with Everton?

   a. 288
   b. 269
   c. 247
   d. 233

19. Who appeared in all 38 matches in the 1998-99 domestic league?

   a. Thomas Myhre
   b. Paul Gerrard
   c. Espen Baardsen
   d. Albert Dunlop

20. 20. In the 2005-06 Premier League season, six different keepers made an appearance.

   a. True
   b. False

QUIZ ANSWERS

1. B – Neville Southall

2. A – True

3. D – Paul Gerrard

4. B – 14

5. C – Bury FC

6. A – Maarten Stekelenburg

7. A – True

8. B – 5

9. D – Leeds United

10. B – 500

11. D – Tranmere Rovers

12. B – False

13. C – Sunderland AFC

14. C – 750

15. D – Richard Wright

16. B – False

17. C – 133

18. B – 269

19. A – Thomas Myhre

20. B – False

DID YOU KNOW?

1. The Everton goalkeepers with the most clean sheets as of March 2021 are as follows: Neville Southall, 269 in 750 appearances; Gordon West, 155 in 402 appearances; Tim Howard, 133 in 414 appearances; Ted Sagar, 120 in 500 appearances; Billy Scott, 94 in 289 appearances; Tom Fern, 67 in 231 appearances; Jimmy O'Neill, 49 in 213 appearances; George Wood, 48 in 126 appearances; Albert Dunlop, 47 in 231 appearances; Dave Lawson, 45 in 152 appearances.

2. Not only was Neville Southall considered by many to be the greatest goalkeeper the Toffees have ever had, but he also holds the club record for appearances with 750, including 578 league outings. He was signed from Bury in July 1981 and originally shared the duties with Jim Arnold. Southall was then loaned to Port Vale but took over as Everton's number-one by the end of 1983. He was also loaned to several teams at the tail-end of his Toffees career before joining Torquay United in 1998. In between, he was named FWA Footballer of the Year in 1985 and helped the team win the European Cup Winners' Cup, two First Division championships, two FA Cups, and three FA Charity Shields while sharing another. He also won runner-up medals in two FA Cup finals, a League Cup final, and the league. Southall was named to the PFA

Team of the Year four straight times and played 92 times for Wales.

3. American international Tim Howard initially joined Everton on a season-long loan from Manchester United in 2006 and signed permanently in February 2007. He went on to play 414 times and posted 133 clean sheets. In August 2012, he set a then-record by playing in 184 Premier League games in a row for the same team, and the season before, he became the fourth Premier League goalie to score when he tallied a goal in a 2-1 home loss to Bolton Wanderers. Howard's streak of 210 straight Premier League appearances came to an end in March 2013, due to a finger injury at just two games short of equaling Neville Southall's club mark. He returned to America in March 2016 to continue his career.

4. Manager David Moyes signed English international Nigel Martyn in September 2003, after the keeper had made a name for himself with Bristol Rovers, Crystal Palace, and Leeds United. He quickly established himself at Goodison Park and was voted by the fans as the 2003-04 Player of the Year. He remained the number-one keeper in 2004-05 but began to suffer ankle problems the next season as Richard Wright took over between the posts. Martyn didn't play again and announced his retirement in June 2006, at the age of 39. His final match for Everton was his 100th for the club.

5. Everton credits Ted Sagar with appearing in exactly 500 official games for the squad between 1930 and 1953, with 120 of those matches resulting in clean sheets. Only Neville Southall played more games in goal with the club than Sagar. He was known for his great ability and fearlessness and joined the side as an apprentice after playing for Thorne Colliery in Yorkshire. Sagar helped the Toffees hoist the First Division title in 1931-32 and 1938-39, as well as the FA Cup in 1932-33. He also played four times for England and once for the Northern Ireland Regional League during World War II.

6. Defender Gordon West decided to try his luck between the posts when he arrived at Blackpool for a trial. The club signed him, and West debuted as a 17-year-old. He was bought by Everton in March 1962 for a reported £27,000 to set a then British transfer record for a goalkeeper. West helped the side capture the 1962-63 First Division and 1963 FA Charity Shield and became the team's first-choice keeper for the next decade. The Toffees won the FA Cup in 1965-66 and the First Division again in 1969-70 with West posting a club-record 21 clean sheets. They also won the 1970 Charity shield. West retired in 1973 after appearing in just over 400 games with the squad but played briefly with local club Tranmere Rovers a few years later.

7. Irish international Billy Scott began his career in his homeland with Cliftonville and Linfield before joining Everton in July 1904. He spent the next eight years with the side, posting 94 clean sheets in 289 contests and

helping it finish as runner-up in the First Division three times. He also reached a pair of FA Cup finals during his stint at Goodison Park with the team winning the trophy in 1905-06 and losing the next season. Scott joined Leeds City in 1912 and then returned to Merseyside to play with Liverpool for a time during the First World War.

8. Another Irish international keeper with Everton was Jimmy O'Neill, who kicked off his career with the team from 1949 to 1960. He helped the Toffees earn promotion to the First Division in 1953-54 after finishing the campaign as runners-up. He made his Everton debut as an 18-year-old in 1950, and the club was relegated to the Second Division after the 1950-51 season. O'Neill reportedly didn't get along very well with new manager Johnny Carey in 1958 but remained with the club until joining Stoke City for a reported £5,000 in July 1960. O'Neill appeared in 213 games with Everton and racked up 49 clean sheets.

9. Tom Fern played 231 times with the Toffees between 1913 and 1924 and pitched in with 67 clean sheets. He joined from Lincoln City and helped the side win the First Division in 1914-15. League football was then put on hold during World War I and resumed in in 1919-20. Fern remained at Goodison Park until joining Port Vale in June 1924 and ended his career with Colwyn Bay United after turning 40 years old.

10. Like Tom Fern, Albert Dunlop tended goal for the Toffees for 231 games. He was signed by the club as a youngster

in 1950 and made his debut with the squad six years later, when beating reigning First Division champions Manchester United 5-2 away to snap United's 26-game undefeated streak. He then beat Arsenal 4-0 in his next outing and became the side's number-one keeper for the next six years. Dunlop helped Everton win the First Division in 1962-63 before joining Wrexham a few weeks later.

CHAPTER 5:

DARING DEFENDERS

QUIZ TIME!

1. Which player made more appearances for Everton?

   a. Brian Labone

   b. Dave Watson

   c. Kevin Ratcliffe

   d. Mick Lyons

2. Yerry Mina scored five goals in the 2019-20 Premier League.

   a. True

   b. False

3. How many goals did David Unsworth tally in the 2000-01 domestic league?

   a. 8

   b. 5

   c. 4

   d. 2

4. Who netted five goals in all competitions in 2015-16?

    a. Séamus Coleman

    b. John Stones

    c. Ramiro Funes Mori

    d. Leighton Baines

5. Which of these players received a red card in the 2016-17 Premier League?

    a. Ashley Williams

    b. Phil Jagielka

    c. Mason Holgate

    d. Matthew Pennington

6. How many goals did Phil Jagielka score in the 2014-15 Premier League?

    a. 6

    b. 3

    c. 7

    d. 4

7. Gary Ablett was the only Everton player shown a red card in the 1992-93 Premier League.

    a. True

    b. False

8. How many appearances did Dave Watson make in all competitions for Everton?

    a. 423

    b. 460

c. 528

d. 559

9. Who led the squad with 10 assists in all competitions in 2009-10?

   a. Leighton Baines

   b. Johnny Heitinga

   c. Phil Neville

   d. Sylvain Distin

10. Which player was shown eight yellow cards in all competitions in 2004-05?

   a. Gary Nasmith

   b. Joseph Yobo

   c. Alessandro Pistone

   d. Tony Hibbert

11. How many appearances did Brian Labone make in all competitions with the side?

   a. 466

   b. 485

   c. 534

   d. 612

12. Dave Watson played in all 38 matches in the 1995-96 Premier League season.

   a. True

   b. False

13. Who made 54 appearances in all competitions in 2007-08?

a. Phil Neville

b. Joleon Lescott

c. Phil Jagielka

d. Tony Hibbert

14. Which player notched three goals in the 1992-93 Premier League?

    a. Ian Snodin

    b. Andy Hinchcliffe

    c. Dave Watson

    d. Matt Jackson

15. How many career games did Kevin Ratcliffe play for the Toffees?

    a. 536

    b. 494

    c. 473

    d. 441

16. Joseph Yobo and Joleon Lescott appeared in all 38 Premier League matches in the 2006-07 season.

    a. True

    b. False

17. Which player was named the club's Player of the Season for 2019-20?

    a. Séamus Coleman

    b. Yerry Mina

    c. Michael Keane

    d. Lucas Digne

18. How many goals did Séamus Coleman score in the 2013-14 domestic league?

    a. 3
    b. 5
    c. 6
    d. 10

19. Which player scored eight goals in all competitions in 1999-2000?

    a. David Weir
    b. Richard Dunne
    c. David Unsworth
    d. Richard Gough

20. Brian Labone scored only two goals in all competitions with Everton.

    a. True
    b. False

QUIZ ANSWERS

1. A – Brian Labone

2. B – False

3. B – 5

4. C – Ramiro Funes Mori

5. A – Ashley Williams

6. D – 4

7. B – False

8. C – 528

9. A – Leighton Baines

10. D – Tony Hibbert

11. C – 534

12. B – False

13. B – Joleon Lescott

14. D – Matt Jackson

15. B – 494

16. A – True

17. D – Lucas Digne

18. C – 6

19. C – David Unsworth

20. A – True

DID YOU KNOW?

1. Former skipper Brian Labone joined in 1957 as a 17-year-old rather than attending university and soon become a key player. The English international spent his entire career at Goodison Park until a serious injury forced him to hang up his boots. However, he remained with the club as an ambassador. Labone played 534 times to currently rank second in all-time for appearances for Everton. He scored just twice but was only booked twice as well. He helped the team win the FA Cup in 1965-66, the First Division title in 1962-63 and 1969-70, and the FA Charity Shield in 1963 and 1970. Labone passed away in 2006 on the way home from an Everton fans awards evening at the age of 66.

2. English international Leighton Baines signed from Wigan Athletic in 2007 and appeared in over 400 games before retiring in 2020. He scored 39 goals and 67 assists while helping the squad reach the FA Cup final in 2008-09. Baines was named to the PFA Premier League Team of the Year for 2011-12 and 2012-13, Premier League and the Everton Player of the Season for 2010-11 and 2012-13, while being named the Everton Players' Player of the Season for 2009-10, 2010-11, and 2012-13. Baines was well known for his free kicks and penalty kicks and won the club's Goal of the Season award for 2010-11. He remained with the Toffees as a youth coach after hanging up his boots.

3. Phil Jagielka was transferred to Everton in July 2007 for a reported £4 million to become the costliest Sheffield United player at the time. Jagielka spent 12 years with the Toffees and became the second-oldest Everton player to score in the Premier League at the age of 36 years and 233 days. He played close to 400 games and chipped in with 19 goals while helping the side reach the FA Cup final in 2008-09. He was named Everton Player of the Season for 2008-09 and 2014-15 and the Players' Player of the Season for 2008-09 while scoring the club's Goal of the Season in 2014-15. Jagielka then returned to Sheffield United in 2019.

4. After starting out as a midfielder, Tony Hibbert converted to a defender and became one of Everton's best. He spent his entire career with his hometown team and won the FA Youth Cup in 1998. He made his first-team debut in March 2001 and played 328 times and remarkably didn't manage to score a goal. Hibbert helped the side reach the 2008-09 FA Cup final, and the right-back became a cult hero at Goodison Park. He was released in 2016 and then announced his retirement.

5. Left-back David Unsworth was nicknamed "Rhino" and also spent time in the Everton youth system. He made his first-team debut in April 1992 and remained with the club until joining West Ham United in 1997. He then joined Aston Villa but returned to Goodison Park from 1998 to 2004 before joining Portsmouth on a free transfer. Unsworth was regarded as a dead-ball expert and chipped

in with 38 goals in just over 320 games. He helped the team capture the 1994-95 FA Cup and the 1995 FA Charity Shield. Unsworth later worked with the club and became a caretaker manager.

6. Séamus Coleman originally played Gaelic football in his Irish Republic homeland before concentrating on soccer. He signed with the Toffees in 2009 from Sligo Rovers and then spent part of 2010 on loan with second-tier side Blackpool. Coleman was handed the captain's armband with Everton in August 2019, and the Irish international has also captained his homeland on numerous occasions. In 2013-14, Coleman was named to the PFA Premier League Team of the Year as well as Everton Players' Player of the Year and Everton Supporters' Player of the Year. As of March 2021, he had played close to 350 games with the team and contributed 26 goals.

7. Although his brother Gary may be more well known, English international Phil Neville was a fine defender in his own right. He joined from Manchester United in 2005 and remained with the club until retiring in 2013. Neville was willing to play wherever needed and served as the club's vice-captain and then captain. In March 2008, he was assaulted by a Liverpool supporter while taking a throw-in during a Merseyside Derby at Anfield. The fan was later banned from all soccer games in England and Wales for three years. Neville appeared in just over 300 games with the squad and later became a television

pundit and football manager. As of 2021, he was the boss of MLS club Inter Miami in America.

8. Nigerian international Joseph Yobo arrived at Everton from Marseille in 2003 after originally joining on loan several months earlier. He soon became a fan favorite and would play every minute of the 2006-07 Premier League campaign. Yobo was named captain for a UEFA Cup game in 2007 when Phil Neville was injured to become the first African to wear the Everton armband. In August 2010, he joined Fenerbahçe in Turkey on loan and soon signed permanently. Yobo played over 200 games with the Toffees, and the former Nigerian captain played 101 times for his country to share its record for appearances.

9. Joining Everton in 1999 from Heart of Midlothian in his homeland, Scottish international David Weir played over 260 games with the side until joining Glasgow Rangers in January 2007. Weir managed to win several individual and team awards in Scotland but went trophy-less with the Toffees. Still, he's considered one of the club's greatest defenders and served as captain between 2005 and 2006. Weir returned to Everton in 2012 as a youth and reserve team coach.

10. Sylvain Distin was a French international who signed with Everton in 2009 from Portsmouth where he was club captain and had won the 2007-08 FA Cup. Distin had also previously played with Paris Saint-Germain, Newcastle United, and Manchester City. He was named Everton

Players' Player of the Year for 2011-12 and formed an effective partnership with Phil Jagielka. After six years and more than 200 appearances with the Toffees, Distin was released in June 2015 and joined AFC Bournemouth.

CHAPTER 6:

MAESTROS OF THE MIDFIELD

QUIZ TIME!

1. Who played more career matches with the Toffees?

    a. John Hurst

    b. Leon Osman

    c. Peter Farrell

    d. Jack Taylor

2. James McCarthy tallied six assists in the 2014-15 Premier League.

    a. True

    b. False

3. Who made 43 appearances in all competitions in 2017-18?

    a. Davy Klaassen

    b. Idrissa Gueye

    c. Tom Davies

    d. Morgan Schneiderlin

4. Which player was shown 10 yellow cards in the 1994-95 Premier League?

    a. John Ebrell
    b. Joe Parkinson
    c. Barry Horne
    d. Vinny Samways

5. How many goals did Kevin Sheedy score with Everton in all competitions?

    a. 76
    b. 88
    c. 97
    d. 105

6. Which player tallied 10 goals in all competitions in 1999-2000?

    a. Michael Ball
    b. Mark Pembridge
    c. John Collins
    d. Nick Barmby

7. Jack Taylor netted 80 goals in all competitions for Everton.

    a. True
    b. False

8. How many goals did John Hurst score with the squad?

    a. 15
    b. 34
    c. 63
    d. 81

9. Which player contributed eight goals in the 2015-16 Premier League?

    a. James McCarthy
    b. Tom Cleverley
    c. Gareth Barry
    d. Ross Barkley

10. How many goals did Leon Osman rack up with Everton in all competitions?

    a. 35
    b. 43
    c. 57
    d. 66

11. Which player made 42 appearances in all competitions in 2012-13?

    a. Marouane Fellaini
    b. Leon Osman
    c. Darron Gibson
    d. Thomas Hitzlsperger

12. Mikel Arteta scored six goals in 13 appearances in the 2009-10 Premier League.

    a. True
    b. False

13. How many appearances did Jack Taylor make in all competitions with Everton?

    a. 356
    b. 384

c. 427

d. 456

14. Who scored five goals in all competitions in 2011-12?

    a. Mikel Arteta

    b. Jack Rodwell

    c. Leon Osman

    d. Marouane Fellaini

15. How many yellow cards was Olivier Dacourt shown in the 1998-99 Premier League?

    a. 17

    b. 13

    c. 10

    d. 6

16. Tim Kilbane played all 38 games in the 2004-05 Premier League season.

    a. True

    b. False

17. Which player made 31 appearances in the 1997-98 Premier League?

    a. Gavin McCann

    b. Gareth Farrelly

    c. John Oster

    d. Nick Barmby

18. How many appearances did Peter Farrell make with Everton in all competitions?

a. 366

b. 418

c. 453

d. 490

19. Which player was shown a red card in the 2007-08 domestic league season?

a. Mikel Arteta

b. Lee Carsley

c. Thomas Gravesen

d. Jack Rodwell

20. Morgan Schneiderlin chipped in with seven goals in all competitions in 2019-20.

a. True

b. False

QUIZ ANSWERS

1. D – Jack Taylor
2. B – False
3. C – Tom Davies
4. A – John Ebrell
5. C – 97
6. D – Nick Barmby
7. A – True
8. B – 34
9. D – Ross Barkley
10. C – 57
11. B – Leon Osman
12. A – True
13. D – 456
14. D – Marouane Fellaini
15. B – 13
16. A – True
17. C – John Oster
18. C – 453
19. A – Mikel Arteta
20. B – False

DID YOU KNOW?

1. Three-time Everton manager Howard Kendall was also a former club captain and one of the side's greatest midfielders. He arrived in 1964 from Preston North End and played just over 270 games with 30 goals to his name before joining Birmingham City in February 1974. Kendall was originally a defender before joining Alan Ball and Colin Harvey to form the "Holy Trinity" in midfield. He helped the Toffees win the First Division title in 1969-70 and the FA Charity Shield in 1970. Kendall returned to Goodison Park as player-manager in 1981 from Blackburn Rovers and hung up his boots after four games to concentrate on managing.

2. Colin Harvey was another excellent Toffees midfielder who would later go on to manage the club. He played with his hometown side from 1963 to 1974 before joining Sheffield Wednesday and netted 24 goals in 387 encounters. He debuted as an 18-year-old three years after joining as an apprentice and helped the team win the 1965-66 FA Cup, the 1969-70 First Division, and 1970 FA Charity Shield. He also collected a runner-up medal for the 1967-68 FA Cup final defeat to West Bromwich Albion. He returned to Goodison Park in 1987 to manage the club until 1990.

3. Playing alongside Howard Kendall and Colin Harvey in Everton's "Holy Trinity" was English international Alan Ball, who joined from Blackpool in 1966 just after winning the World Cup. He helped the team reach the 1967-68 FA Cup final and then capture the 1969-70 First Division title and the 1970 FA Charity Shield. Ball played just over 250 games with the Toffees and scored 79 before being sold to Arsenal in December 1971. He would later play in America, Canada, Australia, and Hong Kong before turning to football management.

4. English international Trevor Steven joined Everton for a reported £300,000 from Burnley as a 19-year-old in 1983 and went on to score 59 goals in 298. He helped the side capture the First Division title in 1984-85 and 1986-87 as well as the FA Cup in 1983-84, the European Cup Winners' Cup in 1984-85, and the FA Charity Shield in 1984, 1985, and 1987 while sharing it in 1986. Steven joined Glasgow Rangers in 1989 and won numerous trophies with the club and later won the French Ligue 1 with Marseille. He then became a television pundit after retiring.

5. Welsh-born Republic of Ireland international Kevin Sheedy arrived from Liverpool in 1982 for a reported £100,000 and contributed 97 goals in 369 games. His greatest achievements were helping the squad win the First Division in 1984-85 and 1986-87 as well as the 1984-85 European Cup Winners' Cup by scoring in the final. He also won three FA Charity Shields and shared a fourth. Sheedy scored numerous goals via direct free-kicks and

was named to the PFA First Division Team of the Year for 1984-85 and 1986-87. Sheedy left for Newcastle United in 1992 on a free transfer but rejoined Everton's coaching staff after hanging up his boots.

6. Barry Horne was a Welsh international captain who played for numerous teams during his pro career, including a stint with the Toffees from 1992 to 1996 after arriving from Southampton. He helped the side hoist the FA Cup in 1994-95 as well as the 1995 FA Charity Shield and suited up 59 times for his country. Horne's most famous Everton goal came during the 1993-94 Premier League finale against Wimbledon when Everton needed a win to avoid relegation. Horne's 30-yard shot tied the game 2-2, enabling Graham Stuart to notch the winner. Horne had also scored the club's first-ever Premier League goal the previous season. He was sold to Birmingham City and later became a media pundit.

7. Danish international Thomas Gravesen was a key player for Everton between 2000 and 2005. He arrived from Hamburger SV and quickly became a fan favorite. He didn't manage to win any silverware with the side but was one of its most consistent performers both at home and in European competition. He was sold to Real Madrid in January 2005 and later joined Glasgow Celtic. Gravesen rejoined Everton on loan from Celtic in 2007 for one final season and played just over 165 games for the team in total.

8. When Thomas Gravesen left for Real Madrid, manager David Moyes replaced him with Spanish international Mikel Arteta by signing him on loan from Real Sociedad in January 2005 and making it a permanent deal six months later. Arteta was then named the club's Player of the Year for 2005-06 and 2006-07 as well as the Players' Player of the Year for 2005-06. The playmaker started his career with Barcelona and had spells with Paris Saint-Germain and Glasgow Rangers. Everton sold him to Arsenal for a reported £10 million in 2011 after scoring 35 goals in just over 200 games. He retired in 2016 and, as of March 2021, was managing Arsenal.

9. Tim Cahill could also play as a striker while with the Toffees from 2004 to 2012, after arriving from Millwall and before joining the New York Red Bulls. He would also go on to play in China, India, and his homeland Australia. Cahill was named one of 50 nominees for the Ballon d'Or after his second season with Everton and helped the side reach the 2008-09 FA Cup final. He's currently the all-time leading goalscorer for Australia with 50 goals in 108 games and was the first Australian to score at a FIFA World Cup. Known for his tremendous heading ability, Cahill led or shared the team in league scoring three times and tallied 68 goals in 278 matches for Everton.

10. After his playing career, South African international Steven Pienaar came back to Goodison Park to join the club as an ambassador. He originally joined in 2007-08 on loan from

Borussia Dortmund and then signed permanently for a reported fee of £2 million. He helped the side reach the 2008-09 FA Cup and was named the Everton Player of the Year for 2009-10. He was sold to Tottenham Hotspur in January 2011 but was reacquired a year later on a six-month loan deal. Pienaar played just 14 games and scored four goals while posting a team-high six assists and signed a permanent transfer in July 2012. He was released after the 2015-16 campaign and joined Sunderland after scoring 28 goals in just under 230 outings.

CHAPTER 7:

SENSATIONAL STRIKERS & FORWARDS

QUIZ TIME!

1. Who made more appearances in all competitions with Everton?

   a. Dixie Dean
   b. Tommy Eglington
   c. Graeme Sharp
   d. Wally Fielding

2. Peter Beardsley scored 13 goals in the 1992-93 Premier League.

   a. True
   b. False

3. How many goals did Oumar Niasse score in the 2017-18 domestic league?

   a. 4
   b. 7
   c. 8
   d. 11

4. Which player scored eight goals in the 2013-14 Premier League?

    a. Steven Pienaar

    b. Gerard Deulofeu

    c. Steven Naismith

    d. Kevin Mirallas

5. Which club did Romelu Lukaku leave to join Everton?

    a. Aston Villa

    b. Liverpool FC

    c. Manchester United

    d. Chelsea FC

6. How many goals did Tim Cahill score in the 2010-11 domestic league?

    a. 11

    b. 9

    c. 7

    d. 5

7. Dominic Calvert-Lewin was the only player to appear in all 38 games in the 2019-20 Premier League.

    a. True

    b. False

8. How many appearances did Graeme Sharp make with Everton in all competitions?

    a. 387

    b. 416

c. 447

d. 532

9. Which side did Graeme Sharp join Everton from?

   a. Queens Park Rangers

   b. Aberdeen United

   c. Stoke City FC

   d. Dumbarton FC

10. Which player made 41 appearances in all competitions in 2004-05?

   a. James Beattie

   b. James McFadden

   c. Marcus Bent

   d. Tim Cahill

11. How many goals did Gylfi Sigurdsson score in the 2018-19 Premier League?

   a. 2

   b. 4

   c. 7

   d. 13

12. Joe-Max Moore tallied six goals in only 15 appearances in the 1999-2000 Premier League.

   a. True

   b. False

13. How many appearances did Dixie Dean make in all competitions with the Toffees?

a. 481

b. 460

c. 433

d. 399

14. Which player netted 28 league goals in 1937-38 to lead the First Division?

a. Dixie Dean

b. Thomas Lawton

c. Wilfred Chadwick

d. Robert Parker

15. Who made 43 appearances in all competitions in 2009-10?

a. Tim Cahill

b. Louis Saha

c. Yakubu Aiyegbeni

d. Diniyar Bilyaletdinov

16. Francis Jeffers was the lone Toffees player to be shown a red card in the 1999-2000 domestic league.

a. True

b. False

17. Which player notched nine goals in all competitions in 2010-11?

a. Louis Saha

b. Diniyar Bilyaletdinov

c. Steve Pienaar

d. Yakubu Aiyegbeni

18. How many appearances did Dixie Dean make for the English men's national team?

    a. 9
    b. 13
    c. 16
    d. 19

19. Which player was shown two red cards in the 1994-95 Premier League campaign?

    a. Paul Rideout
    b. Graham Stuart
    c. Duncan Ferguson
    d. Anders Limpar

20. Romelu Lukaku tallied 30 goals in all competitions in 2016-17.

    a. True
    b. False

QUIZ ANSWERS

1. C – Graeme Sharp

2. B – False

3. C – 8

4. D – Kevin Mirallas

5. D – Chelsea FC

6. B – 9

7. B – False

8. C – 447

9. D – Dumbarton FC

10. C – Marcus Bent

11. B – 4

12. A – True

13. C – 433

14. B – Thomas Lawton

15. A – Tim Cahill

16. B – False

17. A – Louis Saha

18. C – 16

19. C – Duncan Ferguson

20. B – False

DID YOU KNOW?

1. James Vaughan was just 16 years and 270 days old when making his Everton debut in April 2005 and chipped in with a goal late in the game to become the youngest scorer in Premier League history. He appeared to have a great future after winning the Everton Young Player of the Season award for 2006-07. Injuries took their toll, though, and after several loan spells, he joined Norwich City in 2011. Vaughan scored nine times in 60 games for the Toffees, and things may have worked out differently if it wasn't for injuries. However, as of March 2021, Vaughan was playing with Tranmere Rovers and had accumulated 117 goals after 401 career club games and also played for England at the Under-17, -19, and -21 levels.

2. Scottish international Duncan Ferguson enjoyed two stints with Everton and is still with the club as an assistant manager as of March 2021. He joined in 1994 from Glasgow Rangers and played until being sold to Newcastle United in November 1998, after helping the team win the 1994-95 FA Cup. Ferguson was reacquired in 2000 and played with the Toffees until hanging up his boots in 2006. He scored 72 goals in 273 matches with the club while his aggressive style saw him receive eight career red cards in the Premier League. Ferguson's "Duncan Disorderly" nickname seemed perfect considering he was convicted

four times for physical altercations, including once for an on-pitch incident in which he received a three-month jail sentence.

3. Belgian international Romelu Lukaku holds the Everton record for Premier League goals with 68 in 141 games and tallied 87 total in 166 appearances. He's also currently Belgium's highest-ever scorer with 57 goals in his first 89 matches. Lukaku played for the Toffees between 2013 and 2017 after arriving from Chelsea for a reported £31.82 million and leaving for Manchester United for a Toffees-record £76.23 million. He was the first Everton player to score at least 25 goals in two consecutive seasons since Bob Latchford and the first since Dixie Dean to net a goal in nine straight outings at Goodison Park. Lukaku was named Everton's Young Player of the Season and won the Everton Goal of the Season for 2015-16. In 2016-17, he was named to the PFA Premier League Team of the Year and won the Everton Player of the Season and Players' Player of the Season awards.

4. Although English international Gary Lineker played just 57 games for Everton, he was one of the club's most prolific scorers with 40 goals. He was acquired from Leicester City in 1985 and played just one season before joining Barcelona. It was quite a campaign, though, as his 30 league goals saw him win the First Division Golden Boot and included three hat-tricks. Lineker helped the side win the 1985 FA Charity Shield and finish as both First Division and FA Cup runners-up to Liverpool. He

was named the PFA Players' Player of the Year and FWA Footballer of the Year for his lone Toffees season. Lineker scored 48 goals in 80 games for England, and the television pundit is in the English Football Hall of Fame.

5. Scottish international Alex Young joined the club from Heart of Midlothian in November 1960 and went on to score 89 goals in 275 matches before joining Glentoran in Northern Ireland in 1968. Nicknamed "The Golden Vision," Young also scored five times in eight outings for his country. He helped the side win the 1962-63 First Division with his 22 league goals as well as 1963 FA Charity Shield and the 1965-66 FA Cup. Young's son Jason was a pro soccer player in Scotland in the 1990s.

6. After joining the Toffees in July 1946, from Shamrock Rovers along with Peter Farrell, Irish international Tommy Eglington would play 428 games with the team and chip in with 82 goals. His best campaign came in 1952-53 with 16 goals including five in a 7-1 home win over Doncaster Rovers. He also reached double figures in goals in 1953-54 and 1955-56 and helped the side earn promotion by finishing the 1953-54 season as Second Division runner-up. Eglington joined Tranmere Rovers in 1957 and hung up his boots in 1963. He played more Second Division games than any other Everton player.

7. Brian Harris was playing with a non-league club named Port Sunlight before he joined Everton in 1954 for a reported fee of just £10. The versatile Harris played every

position except goalkeeper during his Toffees career and notched 29 goals in 360 outings. He helped the side win the First Division in 1962-63 as well as the 1963 FA Charity Shield and the 1965-66 FA Cup. He was sold to Cardiff City for a reported £10,000 in 1966 and entered football management in 1974 right after hanging up his boots.

8. Everton paid a reported £6,500 to Burnley for Thomas "Tommy" Lawton in January 1937 and also hired his grandfather as deputy groundsman at Goodison Park. He scored on his debut and partnered Dixie Dean during his first season. Lawton began 1937-38 with the reserves but was soon playing center-forward. He led the First Division in scoring with 28 goals and led it again in 1938-39 with 35 goals as Everton won the league crown. Lawton asked to be transferred though in 1939, but World War II meant the Football League was put on hold. He played for the British Army team during the war as well as several other sides including Everton and England. Lawton asked to be transferred again in November 1945 and was sold to Chelsea for a reported £14,000. The member of the English Football Hall of Fame netted 72 goals in 98 official matches with Everton.

9. Nigerian international Victor Anichebe made his debut for the first-team as a teenager in February 2006 and was named the Everton Reserve Player of the Season for 2005-06. He was then named the club's Young Player of the Season for 2006-07. He suffered a serious injury when

fouled by Kevin Nolan of Newcastle United in February 2009 and was sidelined for 11 months. Nolan received a straight red card for the incident and later settled out of court when Anichebe sued for loss of earnings. Anichebe was something of a super-sub for the team as he came off the bench a team-record 95 times before being sold to West Bromwich Albion in 2013.

10. One of the Toffees' top forwards with the current 2020-21 squad is English international Dominic Nathaniel Calvert-Lewin. He joined in August 2016 from Sheffield United for a reported £1.5 million and helped the England national Under-20 team win the 2017 Under-20 World Cup by scoring in the final. He was named the England Under-21 Player of the Year for 2018 and then scored on his senior debut for England in October 2020. Calvert-Lewin netted 15 goals for Everton in 41 matches in 2019-20 and had 19 in his first 31 games in 2020-21 to give him 51 goals in his first 165 appearances with the club.

CHAPTER 8:

NOTABLE TRANSFERS & SIGNINGS

QUIZ TIME!

1. Who was the club's most expensive signing as of 2020?

    a. Richarlison

    b. Gylfi Sigurdsson

    c. Romelu Lukaku

    d. Alex Iwobi

2. Everton did not make an official signing in 2004-05.

    a. True

    b. False

3. Who was the club's most expensive signing in 2015-16?

    a. Morgan Schneiderlin

    b. Aaron Lennon

    c. Oumar Niasse

    d. Ramiro Funes Mori

4. Which side did Everton sign Joseph Yobo from in 2003-04?

a. Olympique Marseille

b. K.R.C. Genk

c. Fulham FC

d. RC Lens

5. Everton sold which player for their largest transfer fee received as of 2020?

    a. John Stones

    b. Marouane Fellaini

    c. Wayne Rooney

    d. Romelu Lukaku

6. How much did the Toffees sell Wayne Rooney for?

    a. £36 million

    b. £33.3 million

    c. £28 million

    d. £25 million

7. Everton signed Yerry Mina from FC Barcelona for a transfer fee of £27.2 million.

    a. True

    b. False

8. Which player did Everton sell to Werder Bremen for a transfer fee of £12 million in 2018-19?

    a. Nikola Vlasic

    b. Ross Barkley

    c. Davy Klaassen

    d. Ademola Lookman

9. Which team did Everton acquire Morgan Schneiderlin from?

   a. Manchester United
   b. Lille OSC
   c. Sunderland AFC
   d. Atalanta

10. What was the transfer fee the Toffees paid to sign Gylfi Sigurdsson?

   a. £37 million
   b. £40 million
   c. £44.46 million
   d. £50 million

11. Who was Everton's most expensive signing in 2006-07?

   a. Phil Jagielka
   b. Leighton Baines
   c. Andy Johnson
   d. Joleon Lescott

12. Everton signed Marouane Fellaini from Belgian club Standard Liège for a transfer fee of £19.58 million.

   a. True
   b. False

13. Which club did the Toffees sell John Stones to?

   a. Arsenal FC
   b. Bayer Leverkusen
   c. Inter Milan
   d. Manchester City

14. How much did the club pay to acquire Richarlison?

    a. £42 million
    b. £35.28 million
    c. £29 million
    d. £26 million

15. Which squad did Everton transfer Mikel Arteta to in 2011-12?

    a. Chelsea FC
    b. Arsenal FC
    c. Liverpool FC
    d. Manchester United

16. Everton transferred Joleon Lescott to Aston Villa for a fee of £12 million.

    a. True
    b. False

17. Which club did Everton transfer Idrissa Gueye to in 2019-20?

    a. Atlético Madrid
    b. Juventus
    c. RB Leipzig
    d. Paris Saint-Germain

18. Which player was the club's most expensive signing in 2013-14?

    a. Muhamed Besic
    b. Kevin Mirallas

c. Arouna Koné

d. James McCarthy

19. What was the transfer fee the Toffees received for selling Romelu Lukaku?

a. £76.23 million

b. £68 million

c. £55 million

d. £52 million

20. Everton signed Gary Speed from Newcastle United for a fee of £7 million.

a. True

b. False

QUIZ ANSWERS

1. B – Gylfi Sigurdsson

2. B – False

3. C – Oumar Niasse

4. A – Olympique Marseille

5. D – Romelu Lukaku

6. B – £33.3 million

7. A – True

8. C – Davy Klaassen

9. A – Manchester United

10. C – £44.46 million

11. C – Andy Johnson

12. A – True

13. D – Manchester City

14. B – £35.28 million

15. B – Arsenal FC

16. B – False

17. D – Paris Saint-Germain

18. D – James McCarthy

19. A – £76.23 million

20. B – False

DID YOU KNOW?

1. The highest transfer fees paid by Everton as of March 2021 have been: Midfielder Gylfi Sigurdsson from Swansea City for £44.46 million in 2017-18; Winger Richarlison de Andrade (Richarlison) from Watford FC for £35.28 million in 2018-19; Striker Romelu Lukaku from Chelsea FC for £31.82 million in 2014-15; Winger Alex Iwobi from Arsenal FC for £27.36 million in 2019-20; Defender Yerry Mina from FC Barcelona for £27.2 million in 2018-19.

2. The highest transfer fees received by Everton as of March 2021 have been: Striker Romelu Lukaku to Manchester United for £76.23 million in 2017-18; Defender John Stones to Manchester City for £50.04 million in 2017-18; Striker Wayne Rooney to Manchester United for £33.3 million in 2004-05; Midfielder Marouane Fellaini to Manchester United for £29.16 million in 2013-14; Midfielder Idrissa Gueye to Paris Saint-Germain for £27 million in 2019-20.

3. Back in August 1966, Everton became the first English club to break the £100,000 transfer barrier when they bought midfielder Alan Ball from Blackpool FC for £110,000. Ball remained with the club until December 22, 1971, when he was transferred to Arsenal FC for a reported £756,000 at the age of 26.

4. Colombian international defender Yerry Mina was acquired from Barcelona for £27.2 million in August 2018.

He scored three goals at the 2018 World Cup to tie a record for goals in a single World Cup tournament by a defender, sharing it with Germans Paul Breitner in 1974 and Andreas Brehme in 1990. Mina's father and uncle were both pro soccer goalkeepers. As of March 2021, the 26-year-old had appeared in 71 games for the Toffees and chipped in with six goals.

5. English international defender Joleon Lescott arrived from Wolverhampton Wanderers for £5.85 million in July 2006 and was Everton's Player of the Season for 2007-08 and the Players' Player of the Season for 2006-07 and 2007-08. Everton rejected two bids for him from Manchester City in 2009. However, Lescott now knew City was interested in him and higher wages were on the horizon. This led him to request a transfer, but manager David Moyes turned him down. Lescott then told Moyes he didn't want to play in the 2009-10 season opener, but he was named to the squad anyway. Moyes dropped Lescott a week later due to his bad attitude and then caved by selling him to City shortly after for £24.75 million.

6. Everton paid £6.12 million for Danish international defender Per Krøldrup from Udinese in Italy in July 2005, and his first six months were spent in the infirmary due to injury. He made his team debut on December 26, 2005, and played 90 minutes at center-back as the squad was thumped 4-0 by Aston Villa. Krøldrup had a brutal game and never played a league game for the side again, even though he was signed to a four-year contract. Krøldrup

was then sold to Fiorentina of Italy in January 2006, for £3.60 million.

7. Midfielder Jose Baxter made his first-team debut in 2008 to become the club's youngest player at the time at the age of 16 years and 191 days. He was loaned to Tranmere Rovers in September 2011 and recalled in January 2012. Baxter rejected a new contract from the club and was released at the end of 2011-12. The England Under-16 and Under-17 player joined Oldham Athletic and then Sheffield United, but in May 2015, he was suspended by Sheffield and the FA after failing a drug test. He was released in May 2016 and rejoined Everton eight months later. After playing for the club's Under-23 team for the season, he was released once again. Baxter rejoined Oldham and was playing in America in 2020.

8. Striker Danny Cadamarteri opened his account with Everton in September 1997, with a highlight-reel goal against Arsenal at the age of 18. He followed up a month later with an even better goal against Liverpool in the famous Merseyside Derby. Toffees fans felt he had a bright future with the club and with England, but his strike against Liverpool was his fourth and final goal he'd score that season. He was loaned to Fulham in November 1999, and in February 2002, Cadamarteri joined Bradford City with the free transfer being made permanent he after he scored on his debut. He played with the England Under-18 and Under-21 squads and notched 15 goals in 110 games with Everton. Cadamerteri was rarely seen in

the Premier League again after 2002 and became a journeyman with stints at numerous lower-tier clubs.

9. Striker Francis Jeffers scored 20 goals in 60 games with Everton from 1997 to 2001 after making his debut as a 16-year-old. The club then sold him to Arsenal in July 2001 for £13.77 million. After scoring just four times in 22 league outings, he was sent back to Everton on loan in September 2003. Jeffers was then sold by Arsenal to Charlton Athletic for £3.51 million. He later played in Scotland, Malta, and Australia before retiring. Jeffers tallied 52 goals in 292 career club contests and was a hit with England's Under-21 squad with a team-high 13 goals in 16 matches. He also scored in his only game with England's senior side. Jeffers returned to Everton in 2016 as a youth coach.

10. Legendary striker Wayne Rooney, who is currently the top all-time scorer for Manchester United and England, started his pro career with Everton from 2002 to 2004 and notched 17 goals in 77 games. He then became the highest-priced teenager in the Premier League when he was sold to Manchester United for £33.3 million as an 18-year-old. He returned to Everton from United on a free transfer in July 2017 and scored 11 goals in 40 games before leaving to play in America. Rooney scored 53 times in 120 matches for England and tallied 253 in 559 outings with United. As of 2020-21, he was managing Derby County.

CHAPTER 9:

ODDS & ENDS

QUIZ TIME!

1. Who is the youngest player to make their debut with the Toffees at 16 years and 176 days old?

    a. Jose Baxter

    b. Thierry Small

    c. James Vaughan

    d. Jake Bidwell

2. The most games Everton won in a Second Division season was 30.

    a. True

    b. False

3. The Toffees' biggest victory in any competition was 11-2 against which club in the 1890 FA Cup?

    a. Derby County FC

    b. Accrington FC

    c. Preston North End

    d. Notts County FC

4. Who is the youngest player to score a hat-trick with Everton?

   a. Wayne Rooney
   b. Stuart Rimmer
   c. Dixie Dean
   d. James Vaughan

5. What is the most wins Everton has recorded in a top-flight season as of 2020?

   a. 22
   b. 26
   c. 29
   d. 31

6. What national record does Everton hold?

   a. Most appearances in the FA Cup final without a win
   b. Most consecutive league games with a goal
   c. Fewest Second Division games to end in a draw
   d. Most seasons played in the top-flight of English football

7. Gary Lineker finished in second place in voting for the Ballon d'Or in 1986.

   a. True
   b. False

8. What is the fewest wins the Toffees have recorded in the Premier League as of 2020?

   a. 14
   b. 10

c. 9

d. 7

9. Everton's biggest defeat in the Premier League was a 7-0 loss to which club?

    a. Chelsea FC

    b. Crystal Palace FC

    c. Swansea City FC

    d. Arsenal FC

10. Who won the PFA Players' Player of the Year award in 1985?

    a. Gary Lineker

    b. Peter Reid

    c. Graeme Sharp

    d. Kevin Sheedy

11. How many games did Everton win in their first season in the Premier League?

    a. 10

    b. 12

    c. 15

    d. 17

12. Goodison Park was the only English league stadium to host a World Cup semifinal game in 1966.

    a. True

    b. False

13. Who was the oldest Everton player at the age of 42 years and 281 days?

a. Neville Southall

b. Dave Watson

c. Ted Sagar

d. Nigel Martyn

14. What was the most losses Everton suffered in a Premier League season as of 2020?

a. 15

b. 24

c. 19

d. 22

15. In 1930-31, Everton tied their record for largest victory in a domestic league match defeating which club 9-1?

a. Southampton FC

b. West Bromwich Albion

c. Tottenham Hotspur

d. Plymouth Argyle

16. The fewest games the Toffees have lost in a league season as of 2020 is seven.

a. True

b. False

17. Which club did Everton host for a club-record highest attendance mark in a league match in 1948?

a. Liverpool FC

b. Manchester United

c. Arsenal FC

d. Chelsea FC

18. What year did Tim Cahill win the Oceania Football Player of the Year award?

    a. 2004
    b. 2006
    c. 2010
    d. 2012

19. Who is the oldest player to score a goal with Everton at 38 years and 305 days old?

    a. Richard Gough
    b. David Ginola
    c. Wally Fielding
    d. Mark Hughes

20. The most points the Toffees have recorded in a top-tier season as of 2020 is 95, in 1986-87.

    a. True
    b. False

QUIZ ANSWERS

1. B – Thierry Small

2. B – False

3. A – Derby County FC

4. C – Dixie Dean

5. C – 29

6. D – Most seasons played in the top-flight of English football

7. A – True

8. C – 9

9. D – Arsenal FC

10. B – Peter Reid

11. C – 15

12. A – True

13. C – Ted Sagar

14. D – 22

15. D – Plymouth Argyle

16. B – False

17. A – Liverpool FC

18. A – 2004

19. C – Wally Fielding

20. B – False

DID YOU KNOW?

1. Everton has been an innovator in the world of soccer with the club being known to be the first for several things in England. These include being the first to: issue a regular match program for home games; to wear numbered shirts from 1-11 (1933 FA Cup final); to have a church attached to its stadium; to install dugouts; to install undersoil heating; to play 4,000 top-flight games; to amass 5,000 league points; to play 100 seasons in the top-flight; to be featured in a pre-recorded TV game in August 1936 versus Arsenal.

2. The team's traditional home colors consist of royal blue shirts, white shorts, and white socks, but in the early years, the squad wore several different colors. They started off by playing in white, then changed to blue and white stripes and then to black shirts. When the club moved to Goodison Park in 1892, the colors became salmon pink and dark blue striped shirts with dark blue shorts and then ruby shirts with blue trim and dark blue shorts. Royal blue shirts with white shorts were first used in the 1901-02 season. Sky blue shirts were worn in 1906, but after a protest by the fans, they reverted to royal blue.

3. The club's traditional away kit consisted of white shirts with black shorts. However, after 1968, they wore amber shirts and royal blue shorts on many occasions. Various different combinations of colors were then worn during

the 1970s and 1980s, and the team has also been known to wear black, white, grey, and yellow away shirts.

4. The club's most common nickname is "The Toffees" or "The Toffeemen." These came about after moving to Goodison Park and are believed to be linked to a Toffee Lady tradition in which a girl walked around the perimeter of the pitch before kickoff while tossing Everton Mints to the fans. Other historians believe the nicknames were introduced because Ye Anciente Everton Toffee House was located close to the Queen's Head Hotel where the club often held meetings.

5. Over the years, Everton has been known by several other nicknames. The team was known as "The Black Watch" when the black kit was worn and then were known as "The Blues." The squad that won the 1994-95 FA Cup was known as "The Dogs of War," and when David Moyes was appointed manager, he called Everton "The People's Club," which has also been used as a nickname.

6. The team originally played its matches in the southeast corner of Stanley Park with the first official outing being in 1879. A man named J. Cruitt then donated land at Priory Road in 1882, and it became the club's new home. Everton then played at Anfield in 1884 in exchange for a rental fee of £100 a year. However, by 1888, the rent had increased to £240 a year, and the club decided to leave in 1892 due to the rising cost.

7. Everton FC member John Houlding attempted to gain full control of the club and registered it as Everton FC and Athletic Grounds Ltd. He attempted to take over the Everton name, team colors, fixtures, and league position, but the Football Association denied him. Houlding then decided to form a new club which became Liverpool FC.

8. Goodison Park was the first major soccer stadium erected in England and was opened in 1892. It was the first venue in England to install undersoil heating and the first to have two tiers on all sides. Since 1962, the team's players have walked onto the pitch to a song named "Johnny Todd," which is regarded as a traditional Liverpool children's song.

9. Everton is planning to build a new 52,000 capacity stadium on the Liverpool waterfront at the Bramley-Moore Dock site. The proposal for a new ground received council approval in February 2021, and the club is hoping to host games there by 2024. The £500 million venue has to be approved by the UK government before it proceeds though.

10. The club entered the UK pop singles chart four times in the 1980s and 1990s when several English teams released songs to celebrate reaching the FA Cup final. In 1984, the song named "The Boys in Blue" reached number 82 on the chart, while the song "Here We Go" peaked at number 14 the following year. In 1986, the song "Everybody's Cheering the Blues" reached number 83, and in 1995, the team re-

recorded "All Together Now," which was originally recorded by Liverpool band The Farm, and it peaked at number 27.

CHAPTER 10:

DOMESTIC COMPETITION

QUIZ TIME!

1. Which season did Everton finish as runner-up in the English Football League Super Cup?

    a. 1981-82
    b. 1985-86
    c. 1989-90
    d. 1993-94

2. The first time Everton reached the FA Cup final was in 1892-93.

    a. True
    b. False

3. Which season did Everton win its first First Division title?

    a. 1914-15
    b. 1904-05
    c. 1890-91
    d. 1889-90

4. The Toffees faced which club in the 1995 FA Charity Shield?

   a. Stoke City
   b. Manchester United
   c. Blackburn Rovers
   d. Newcastle United

5. How many times has Everton won the First Division/ Premier League as of 2020?

   a. 12
   b. 9
   c. 7
   d. 5

6. Which side did Everton face in the 1977 League Cup final?

   a. Aston Villa
   b. Manchester City
   c. Queens Park Rangers
   d. Stoke City

7. Everton won the 1988-89 League Cup.

   a. True
   b. False

8. Which club did the Toffees defeat to win their first FA Cup?

   a. Bristol Rovers
   b. Queens Park Rangers
   c. Fulham FC
   d. Newcastle United

9. How many times has Everton captured the FA Cup as of 2020?

    a. 10
    b. 7
    c. 5
    d. 3

10. The Toffees shared the 1986 FA Charity Shield honors with which club?

    a. Liverpool FC
    b. Tottenham Hotspur
    c. Wolverhampton Wanderers
    d. Aston Villa

11. Which player was named Man of the Match in the 1994-95 FA Cup final?

    a. Dave Watson
    b. Neville Southall
    c. Andy Hinchcliffe
    d. Graham Stuart

12. Everton won the Premier League in 1994-95.

    a. True
    b. False

13. Which season did the Toffees win the Second Division title?

    a. 1960-61
    b. 1951-52

c. 1930-31

d. 1928-29

14. Everton downed which squad in the 1983-84 FA Cup final?

    a. Southampton FC

    b. Plymouth Argyle

    c. Sheffield Wednesday

    d. Watford FC

15. How many times has Everton competed in the League Cup final as of 2020?

    a. 7

    b. 2

    c. 10

    d. 5

16. Everton played in the Full Members' Cup final twice.

    a. True

    b. False

17. Who was the winner of the Toffees' Goal of the Season award for 2005-06?

    a. Leon Osman

    b. Leighton Baines

    c. James Beattie

    d. Dan Gosling

18. Which year did Everton win their first FA Charity Shield?

    a. 1974

    b. 1957

c. 1928

d. 1921

19. Who won the club's 2005-06 Player of the Season award?

    a. Leighton Baines
    b. Phil Jagielka
    c. Joleon Lescott
    d. Mikel Arteta

20. Everton was the first winner of the FA Cup.

    a. True
    b. False

QUIZ ANSWERS

1. B – 1985-86

2. A – True

3. C – 1890-91

4. C – Blackburn Rovers

5. B – 9

6. A – Aston Villa

7. B – False

8. D – Newcastle United

9. C – 5

10. A – Liverpool FC

11. A – Dave Watson

12. B – False

13. C – 1930-31

14. D – Watford FC

15. B – 2

16. A – True

17. C – James Beattie

18. C – 1928

19. D – Mikel Arteta

20. B – False

DID YOU KNOW?

1. As of the conclusion of the 2019-20 season, Everton has won nine top-tier league titles, five FA Cups, one second-tier league championship, and nine FA Charity/Community Shield trophies. The club has also hoisted the FA Youth Cup on three occasions in 1964-65, 1983-84, and 1997-98.

2. The team won the First Division in 1890-91, 1914-15, 1927-28, 1931-32, 1938-39, 1962-63, 1969-70, 1984-85, and 1986-87. The squad finished as runner-up in 1889-90, 1894-95, 1901-02, 1904-05, 1908-09, 1911-12, and 1985-86. The FA Cup was won in 1905-06, 1932-33, 1965-66, 1983-84, and 1994-95, while they were runners-up in 1892-93, 1896-97, 1906-07, 1967-68, 1984-85, 1985-86, 1988-89, and 2008-09.

3. Everton was crowned champions of the second-tier Second Division in 1930-31 and finished as runner-up in 1953-54. The club has yet to win an English League Cup but finished as runner-up in 1976-77 and 1983-84. The side won the FA Charity/Community Shield in 1928, 1932, 1963, 1970, 1984, 1985, 1987, and 1995 and shared it in 1986.

4. Since 2006, the club has given out an official Player of the Season award with the winners being: Mikel Arteta, 2005-06; Mikel Arteta, 2006-07; Joleon Lescott, 2007-08; Phil Jagielka, 2008-09; Steven Pienaar, 2009-10; Leighton Baines, 2010-11; John Heitinga, 2011-12; Leighton Baines, 2012-13; Séamus Coleman, 2013-14; Phil Jagielka, 2014-15; Gareth

Barry, 2015-16; Romelu Lukaku, 2016-17; Jordan Pickford, 2017-18; Lucas Digne, 2018-19; Richarlison, 2019-20.

5. The Players' Player of the Season awards have been won by: Mikel Arteta, 2005-06; Joleon Lescott, 2006-07; Joleon Lescott, 2007-08; Phil Jagielka, 2008-09; Leighton Baines, 2009-10; Leighton Baines, 2010-11; Sylvain Distin, 2011-12; Leighton Baines, 2012-13; Séamus Coleman, 2013-14; Phil Jagielka, 2014-15; Gareth Barry, 2015-16; Romelu Lukaku, 2016-17; Jordan Pickford, 2017-18; Lucas Digne and Idrissa Gana Gueye, 2018-19; Mason Holgate, 2019-20.

6. The club's Young Player of the Season award has been won by: James McFadden, 2005-06; James Vaughan, 2006-07; Victor Anichebe, 2007-08; Marouane Fellaini, 2008-09; Jack Rodwell, 2009-10; Séamus Coleman, 2010-11; Apostolos Vellios, 2011-12; Ross Barkley, 2012-13; Ross Barkley, 2013-14; John Stones, 2014-15; Romelu Lukaku, 2015-16; Tom Davies, 2016-17; Jordan Pickford, 2017-18; Richarlison, 2018-19; Mason Holgate, 2019-20.

7. Those who have been honored with the Goal of the Season award have been: James Beattie, 2005-06; James McFadden, 2006-07; Leon Osman, 2007-08; Dan Gosling, 2008-09; Diniyar Bilyaletdinov, 2009-10; Leighton Baines, 2010-11; Phil Neville, 2011-12; Kevin Mirallas, 2012-13; Ross Barkley, 2013-14; Phil Jagielka, 2014-15; Romelu Lukaku, 2015-16; Tom Davies, 2016-17; Wayne Rooney, 2017-18; Gylfi Sigurdsson, 2018-19; Leighton Baines, 2019-20.

8. The most goals scored by an Everton player in a match is six by Jack Southworth against West Bromwich Albion in 1893. The most goals tallied in a season is 60 by Dixie Dean in 1927-28. Bertie Freeman currently holds the team record for goals in consecutive games at 10 in 1908. The youngest goalscorer has been James Vaughn against Crystal Palace in 2005 when he was 16 years and 270 days old. The oldest goalscorer has been Wally Fielding against West Bromwich Albion in 1958 at the age of 38 years and 305 days.

9. The players who have made the most all-time appearances for Everton, as of March 2021, have been: Neville Southall, 750; Brian Labone, 534; Dave Watson, 528; Ted Sagar, 500; Kevin Ratcliffe, 494; Mick Lyons, 472; Jack Taylor, 456; Peter Farrell, 453; Graeme Sharp, 447; Leon Osman, 433; Dixie Dean, 433.

10. Everton's current record for the biggest home victory is 11-2 versus Derby County in the FA Cup in 1890, while their biggest away win has been a 7-0 thumping of Charlton Athletic in 1931. The team's record league defeat is 7-0 to Sunderland in 1934 as well as to Wolverhampton Wanderers in 1939 and to Arsenal in 2005. Their biggest FA Cup defeat is 6-0 to Crystal Palace in the first round in 1922.

CHAPTER 11:

EUROPE & BEYOND

QUIZ TIME!

1. What was the first team Everton faced in European competition?

    a. FC Zbrojovka Brno

    b. AS Roma

    c. Dunfermline Athletic

    d. FC Aris Bonnevoie

2. Everton has won one major European tournament as of 2020.

    a. True

    b. False

3. Who is the club's leading goalscorer in European competitions as of 2020?

    a. Andy Gray

    b. Andy Johnson

    c. Fred Pickering

    d. Romelu Lukaku

4. What was the first international competition the Toffees participated in?

    a. European Cup Winners' Cup
    b. UEFA Cup
    c. European Cup
    d. Inter-Cities Fairs Cup

5. Which club did Everton NOT play against in the 1970-71 European Cup?

    a. Borussia Mönchengladbach
    b. SK Slovan Bratislava
    c. Panathinaikos FC
    d. Keflavík

6. Which player has made the most appearances in European competitions for Everton as of 2020?

    a. Leon Osman
    b. Tony Hibbert
    c. Tim Howard
    d. Brian Labone

7. As of 2020, the Toffees have won one international double.

    a. True
    b. False

8. Which club did Everton defeat to win the 1984-85 European Cup Winners' Cup?

    a. FK Inter Bratislava
    b. Fortuna Sittard

c. Bayern Munich

d. SK Rapid Wien

9. How many goals did Fred Pickering score with the Toffees in European competitions?

   a. 10

   b. 6

   c. 12

   d. 8

10. What was the first team Everton played in the European Cup?

   a. AS Monaco

   b. SL Benfica

   c. Real Madrid

   d. Inter Milan

11. The Toffees were eliminated by which club in the second round of the 1978-79 UEFA Cup?

   a. FK Dukla Prague

   b. Finn Harps FC

   c. Feyenoord

   d. AC Milan

12. Andy Gray scored five goals in only three European matches.

   a. True

   b. False

13. How many appearances did Tony Hibbert make with the Toffees in European competitions?

a. 13

b. 18

c. 24

d. 30

14. Who scored the winning goal in the 1984-85 European Cup Winners' Cup final?

    a. Kevin Sheedy

    b. Trevor Steven

    c. Andy Gray

    d. Graeme Sharp

15. How many goals did Romelu Lukaku score with Everton in European competitions?

    a. 14

    b. 10

    c. 5

    d. 8

16. Everton was eliminated by FC Shalke 04 in the quarterfinals of the 2005-06 UEFA Cup.

    a. True

    b. False

17. Who scored the Toffees' first goal in a European competition?

    a. Roy Vernon

    b. Alex Young

    c. Dennis Stevens

    d. Brian Harris

18. How many appearances did Tim Howard make in European competitions with the Toffees?

    a. 35
    b. 28
    c. 23
    d. 19

19. Everton's biggest European victory was 6-1 against which club in the 2007-08 UEFA Cup?

    a. SK Brann
    b. FC Nürnberg
    c. AEL FC
    d. Villarreal FC

20. 20. Everton has won 60 games in all UEFA competitions as of 2020.

    a. True
    b. False

QUIZ ANSWERS

1. C – Dunfermline Athletic

2. A – True

3. D – Romelu Lukaku

4. D – Inter-Cities Fairs Cup

5. B – SK Slovan Bratislava

6. C – Tim Howard

7. A – True

8. D – SK Rapid Wien

9. B – 6

10. D – Inter Milan

11. A – FK Dukla Prague

12. A – True

13. C – 24

14. B – Trevor Steven

15. D – 8

16. B – False

17. C – Dennis Stevens

18. B – 28

19. A – SK Brann

20. B – False

DID YOU KNOW?

1. Everton's first entry into European competition came in 1963-64 when they played in the European Cup. Their most recent appearance came in 2017-18 when they competed in the UEFA Europa League. The club's one and only European trophy as of 2021 was the 1984-85 European Cup Winners' Cup. The side has competed in 18 major European tournaments as of 2020-21.

2. The team has competed in the European (Inter-Cities) Fairs Cup three times in 1962-63, 1964-65, and 1965-66. They played in the European Cup in 1963-64, 1970-71 and the Champions League in 2005-06. They participated in the European/UEFA Cup Winners' Cup in 1966-67, 1984-85, and 1995-96. They played in the UEFA Cup in 1975-76, 1978-79, 1979-80, 2005-06, 2007-08, and 2008-09 and competed in the Europa League in 2009-10, 2014-15, and 2017-18.

3. The European Cup Winners' Cup victory took place on May 15, 1985, in front of 38,500 fans in Rotterdam, Holland. Everton took on Rapid Vienna of Austria and came away with a 3-1 triumph. Andy Gray opened the scoring in the 57th minute with Trevor Steven doubling the lead 15 minutes later. Johann Krankl narrowed the gap for Vienna in the 83rd minute, but Kevin Sheedy restored Everton's two-goal bulge in the 85th.

4. The squad managed to reach the quarterfinals of the European Cup in 1970-71 where they were beaten on the away goals rule by Panathinaikos of Greece. The first leg ended in a 1-1 draw at Goodison Park, with the second leg ending 0-0 in Greece. Everton had downed Keflavik of Iceland 9-2 on aggregate in the first round of the competition and then edged Borussia Mönchengladbach 4-3 in a penalty shootout after their two-legged tie ended 2-2 on aggregate.

5. The players with the most European appearances for Everton, as of March 2021, are: Goalkeeper Tim Howard 28; Leon Osman 25; Leighton Baines 25; Tony Hibbert 24; Phil Jagielka 23; Brian Labone 19; Tim Cahill 19; Colin Harvey 19; Joseph Yobo 19; Johnny Morrissey 18; Phil Neville 18; Yakubu Ayegbeni 18.

6. The club's top scorers in European competitions are as follows: Romelu Lukaku, eight goals in nine games; Fred Pickering, six goals in nine games; Andy Gray, five goals in three games; Andy King, four goals in five games; Joe Royle, four goals in six games; Andy Johnson, four goals in seven games; Graeme Sharp, four goals in eight games; Alan Ball, four goals in 10 games; Victor Anichebe, four goals in 11 games; Mikel Arteta, four goals in 14 games; Yakubu Ayegbeni, four goals in 17 games; Tim Cahill, four goals in 19 games; Phil Jagielka, four goals in 23 games.

7. Everton's first European match was a 1-0 victory over Dunfermline FC in the European Fairs Cup on September

25, 1962. Their record European victory was 6-1 over SK Brann in the UEFA Cup Round-of-32 on February 21, 2008. The biggest aggregate European win was 10-0 versus Finn Harps in the UEFA Cup First Round in 1978. The club's highest home attendance for a European contest has been 62,408 versus Inter Milan in the European Cup First Round-First Leg on September 18, 1963.

8. As of 2020-21, Everton's combined record in the European Cup/Champions League, Europa League, Cup Winners' Cup, and European Fairs cup is 91 games played; 47 wins, 19 draws, 25 losses, with 148 goals scored and 99 goals against for a winning percentage of 51.6.

9. Everton's worst season in Europe came in 2005-06. They were beaten 4-2 by Villarreal in the third qualifying round after losing both the home and away leg 2-1. They then entered the UEFA Cup and were drilled 5-2 on aggregate by Dinamo Bucuresti of Romania. They were 1-0 winners at home in the first leg but were trounced 5-1 in Bucharest in the second leg.

10. The biggest aggregate victory in Europe for Everton took place in the 1978-79 UEFA Cup. They thumped Finn Harps of the Republic of Ireland 10-0 in the first round after winning both the home and away legs 5-0. They then met Dukla Prague of the Czech Republic in the second round and were eliminated on the away goals rule after winning 2-1 at home in the first leg and losing 1-0 away in the second leg.

CHAPTER 12:

TOP SCORERS

QUIZ TIME!

1. Who is Everton's all-time leader in goals in all competitions?

    a. Dixie Dean

    b. Graeme Sharp

    c. Bob Latchford

    d. Alex Young

2. Everton has had 10 different players lead the English top-tier in scoring as of 2020.

    a. True

    b. False

3. Who was the first player to lead the Toffees in scoring in the Football League?

    a. John Bell

    b. Alex Latta

    c. Edgar Chadwick

    d. Fred Geary

4. How many goals did Tony Cottee score to lead Everton in their inaugural Premier League season?

   a. 15
   b. 12
   c. 9
   d. 7

5. Who led the First Division with 30 goals in 1985-86?

   a. Adrian Heath
   b. Trevor Steven
   c. Graeme Sharp
   d. Gary Lineker

6. How many seasons did Dixie Dean lead the Toffees in scoring?

   a. 5
   b. 7
   c. 10
   d. 12

7. Romelu Lukaku led the Premier League in scoring in 2016-17.

   a. True
   b. False

8. How many goals did Alex "Sandy" Young score in all competitions for the Toffees?

   a. 99
   b. 109

c. 117

d. 125

9. Which player holds the club record for most goals in a game with six against West Bromwich Albion in 1893?

a. Billy Stewart

b. Jack Southworth

c. Alan Maxwell

d. Edgar Chadwick

10. How many goals did Graeme Sharp notch in all competitions with Everton?

a. 144

b. 159

c. 183

d. 210

11. Which player won the Golden Boot two years in a row with Everton in 1937-38 and 1938-39?

a. Ephraim Dodds

b. John Parker

c. Eddie Wainwright

d. Thomas Lawton

12. Dixie Dean scored 60 goals in the 1927-28 season, which still stands as the record for most goals in an English top-flight season.

a. True

b. False

13. Which two players led Everton with eight goals each in the 2008-09 Premier League?

    a. Marouane Fellaini and Tim Cahill
    b. Louis Saha and Mikel Arteta
    c. Leon Osman and Yakubu
    d. Jô and Mikel Arteta

14. How many goals did Bob Latchford score to win a 1977-78 Golden Boot?

    a. 42
    b. 36
    c. 30
    d. 27

15. Who holds the club record for most goals in the Premier League as of 2020?

    a. Gylfi Sigurdsson
    b. Tim Cahill
    c. Marouane Fellaini
    d. Romelu Lukaku

16. James Settle was the first Everton player to lead the league in scoring.

    a. True
    b. False

17. How many goals did Dixie Dean score with Everton in all competitions?

    a. 312
    b. 347

c. 383

d. 396

18. Which player led the club with 12 goals in the 1999-2000 Premier League?

   a. Kevin Campbell

   b. Duncan Ferguson

   c. Andrei Kanchelskis

   d. Tomasz Radzinski

19. How many Premier League goals did Romelu Lukaku tally with Everton?

   a. 73

   b. 68

   c. 56

   d. 51

20. Wayne Rooney never finished a season as Everton's top scorer.

   a. True

   b. False

QUIZ ANSWERS

1. A – Dixie Dean

2. A – True

3. C – Edgar Chadwick

4. B – 12

5. D – Gary Lineker

6. C – 10

7. B – False

8. D – 125

9. B – Jack Southworth

10. B – 159

11. D – Thomas Lawton

12. A – True

13. A – Marouane Fellaini and Tim Cahill

14. C – 30

15. D – Romelu Lukaku

16. B – False

17. C – 383

18. A – Kevin Campbell

19. B – 68

20. B – False

DID YOU KNOW?

1. Everton players have managed to lead the top-tier of English soccer in scoring a record 12 times. However, none of these have come in the Premier League era. Those who led the First Division in goals over the years have been: John Southworth, 27 in 1983-94; James Settle, 18 in 1901-02; Alexander "Sandy" Young, 28 in 1906-07; Bertram Freeman, 38 in 1908-09; Robert Parker, 36 in 1914-15; Wilfred Chadwick, 28 in 1923-24; William "Dixie" Dean, 60 in 1927-28; William "Dixie" Dean, 45 in 1931-32; Thomas Lawton, 28 in 1937-38; Thomas Lawton, 34 in 1938-39; Bob Latchford, 30 in 1977-78; Gary Lineker, 30 in 1985-86.

2. In the 1927-28 campaign, 21-year-old William Ralph "Dixie" Dean netted 60 league goals in just 39 contests to set a record that's unlikely to be broken in the English top-tier. In fact, he scored 85 times during the 1928 calendar year. Dean is the club's all-time leading scorer with 383 goals in 433 outings and led the First Division in scoring in 1927-28 and 1931-32 with Everton winning the league both seasons. Dean played with the team from 1925 to 1937 and also scored 18 goals in 16 games for England. This member of the English Football Hall of Fame also won a Second Division title with the Toffees as well as two FA Charity Shields and an FA Cup. He sadly passed away in 1980 after watching Everton play Liverpool at Goodison Park.

3. Scottish international striker Graeme Sharp arrived at Everton from Dumbarton in 1980 and was just a part-time player during his first season. However, he became a regular under manager Howard Kendall in his second campaign and went on to notch 159 goals in 447 games and led the team in scoring four times. He also helped the side capture the First Division title in 1984-85 and 1986-87 as well as the 1983-84 FA Cup, the 1984-85 European Cup Winners' Cup, and four FA Charity Shields. Sharp joined Oldham Athletic in 1991 and later became player-manager of the club. After retiring, he would return to Everton as a club ambassador.

4. After kicking off his career with Birmingham City, English international striker Bob Latchford joined the Toffees for a British-record transfer fee of £350,000 in 1974 with Howard Kendall and Archie Styles both leaving Everton for Birmingham in the transaction. Latchford led the squad in scoring five straight seasons and topped the First Division in 1977-78 with 30 goals. He didn't manage to win any silverware with Everton, with the closest attempt being a runner-up medal for the 1976-77 League Cup. However, he tallied 138 goals in 286 contests before joining Swansea City in 1981. His brothers Dave and Peter Latchford were both professional goalkeepers in the UK.

5. Alexander "Sandy" Young arrived at Goodison Park from Falkirk in his native Scotland in 1901 and went on to score the lone goal in the 1905-06 FA Cup final and led the First Division in scoring the next season with 28 goals. Young

notched 125 goals in 314 Everton matches and led the team in scoring in six of eight seasons before joining Tottenham Hotspur in 1911. Young was convicted of manslaughter in the death of his brother in Australia in 1916 and received a three-year prison sentence. He passed away in an Edinburgh, Scotland, asylum in 1959.

6. Joe Royle was well known for managing the Toffees from 1994 to 1997 but was also one of the side's greatest players and goalscorers. He began his pro career with his hometown club in 1966 and went on to net 119 goals in 273 appearances. Royle was just 16 years old when making his debut and led the team in scoring in four straight seasons. His 23 league goals in 1969-70 helped the side win the First Division title, and he also won the FA Charity Shield in 1970. He joined Manchester City in 1974 for a reported £170,000, but a knee injury forced him to hang up his boots in 1982 at the age of 33. The English international then turned to football management.

7. Only Dixie Dean had a better scoring record for Everton than Roy "Taffy" Vernon when it comes to goals-per-game for the club's top-10 scorers. The Welsh international forward Vernon contributed 111 goals in 203 outings for 0.55 goals-per-contest, while Dean scored 0.88 goals-per-game. He joined in 1960 from Blackburn Rovers and became an instant hit by tallying nine goals in his first 12 contests and led the side in scoring four straight seasons. He captained the squad which won the First Division title in 1962-63 and the 1963 Charity Shield, but by 1965, he was

sold to Stoke City for a reported £40,000. Vernon, who was an expert penalty-taker, later played in America and South Africa.

8. Dave Hickson currently sits tied with Roy Vernon in the club's all-time scoring list with 111 goals, achieving the feat in 243 games. He debuted in 1951, three years after signing with the club, due to his military service. His 25 goals in 1953-54 helped the team earn promotion to the First Division as Second Division runner-up, but he was then sold to Aston Villa for a reported £17,500 in 1955. Hickson was reacquired by the Toffees in 1957 for a reported £7,500 from Huddersfield Town and then sold to Liverpool two years later. He became a football manager after retiring as a player.

9. One of Everton's earliest scoring stars was 5-foot-6-inch tall English international forward Edgar "Hooky" Chadwick with 110 goals in 310 games. He signed in July 1888 from Blackburn Rovers and was just over 19 years old when making his debut. He was the only squad player to appear in all 22 league games during the Football League's inaugural 1888-89 campaign and led it in scoring with six goals. The team finished as First Division runner-up in 1889-90 and won the league title the following season. Chadwick joined Burnley in 1899 and would later manage the Dutch national men's team to bronze medals at the 1908 and 1912 Olympic Games. His cousin Arthur Chadwick played for England and Southampton, and his cousin Albert Chadwick played for Everton.

10. English international forward Tony Cottee finished his Everton career one goal shy of the century mark as he tallied 99 times in 206 appearances. He joined in August 1988 for a reported £2.2 million from West Ham United and scored a hat-trick on his league debut. The side reached the FA Cup final in his first season but fell 3-2 to Liverpool in extra time. Cottee returned to West Ham in September 1994 for defender David Burrows and cash. Cottee later played in Malaysia, dabbled in football management and broadcasting, and also made a cameo appearance in a 2018 film called *Final Score*.

CONCLUSION

It's hard to believe, but Everton FC will be celebrating the 150th anniversary of the founding of the club in 2028. After being formed in 1878, the team has been one of the most consistent in the UK by playing all but four seasons in the top-flight of the English league.

You've just read through the captivating history of the Toffees from their days at Stanley Park, Priory Road, and Anfield to their permanent home at Goodison Park.

With the club being formed so long ago, it was impossible to include everybody in the book, but we hope most of your favorites are represented in some shape or form.

We hope you've enjoyed taking a look back at the team's marvellous history in this lighthearted and entertaining manner and would be pleased if you've learned something new along the way.

Armed with 12 different quiz chapters and a myriad of "Did you Know?" facts, you should now be as ready as ever to successfully challenge fellow Evertonians and other soccer fans to an assortment of quiz contests.

We've included as many of the team's top players and managers as possible and provided a collection of informative and educational facts and trivia regarding the club's records, silverware, transfers, and achievements.

We also hope you'll be inclined to share the trivia book with others to help teach the history of Everton FC to those who may not be aware of it.

The ongoing story of Everton is sure to be just as entertaining as the first century or so, and with passionate and loyal fans like you, it will hopefully be just as successful.

Thanks kindly for reading the book and supporting the Toffees over the years.

Printed in Great Britain
by Amazon